HOME LINK-UP

Heinemann Educational,
Halley Court, Jordan Hill, Oxford OX2 8EJ
a division of Reed Educational and Professional Publishing Ltd

OXFORD   FLORENCE   PRAGUE   MADRID   ATHENS
MELBOURNE   AUCKLAND   KUALA LUMPUR   SINGAPORE   TOKYO
IBADAN   NAIROBI   KAMPALA   JOHANNESBURG   GABORONE
PORTSMOUTH NH (USA)   CHICAGO   MEXICO CITY   SAO PAULO

ISBN 0 435 02122 2

97 98 99 00 01
10 9 8 7 6 5 4 3 2 1
Design and produced by Oxprint Ltd
Printed in the UK by Athenaeum Press Ltd, Newcastle-upon-Tyne

Writing Team
John T Blair
Ian K Clark
Aileen P Duncan
Percy W Farren
Archie MacCallum
Myra A Pearson
Dorothy S Simpson
John W Thayers

DeJS Pre-Prep

Contents

Introduction i
　　Using Home Link-up i
　　Guidance for Parents iv
　　Record Sheet v
　　Answers are provided at the back of the book

Activities	Linked to

Number

Addition, subtraction to 20

Place Value, Addition to 99

Subtraction to 99

Multiplication

Division

Fractions

Division

Measure

Time

Length

Area

Shape

3D Shape

Tiling, Symmetry

Handling data

Extra

Extra activities are provided after 17, 28 and 52.

Introduction

Heinemann Mathematics 3 Home Link-up contains 60 homework activities linked to specific pages of the core Workbooks and Textbook for this stage of the course.

Teachers can use the activities to provide children with valuable practice at home, related to their work in school. The activities are aimed mainly at consolidating techniques and providing opportunities to apply them. Some activities include problem solving questions. There are also three *Extra* activities, not specifically referenced to the Workbooks or Textbook which provide additional challenges for some children.

For parents, Home Link-up provides
— the reassurance of a consistent and positive approach to mathematics homework
— an insight into some of the mathematics carried out in school
— an opportunity to talk to their children about mathematics
— a focus for communication with the school.

For children, the activities
— provide opportunities for individual work
— help to develop good home study habits
— encourage responsibility for learning.

The activities are presented as photocopiable sheets. The booklet also includes
— a contents list
— advice for teachers about using the materials
— answers
— a page of guidance for parents
— a record sheet.

USING HOME LINK-UP

Homework activities

■ The activities are intended for children who can benefit from spending more time at home consolidating recently completed or current work in school. They are *not* suitable for children who require further teaching of a topic before they attempt related homework activities.

■ Some pages contain two activities, not necessarily of the same length or dealing with the same topics. Other pages contain just one. The underlying principle is that each activity contains work which might take a child 15 to 20 minutes to complete at home.

■ The activities are numbered from 1 to 60. A reference to the relevant pages of the Heinemann Mathematics 3 Workbooks or Textbook is given in the heading for each activity. For example:

Name	Heinemann Mathematics 3 Home Link-up Workbook 1, page 6	3
	Addition facts for 15	

The mathematics contained in each activity is also described in its heading. Activities often cover content related to more than one page of a Workbook or the Textbook.

- There are no references to curricular guidelines or teaching notes for the activities in Home Link-up. The appropriate references are those of the core Workbooks and Textbook pages to which the activities are linked.

Special features

- The activities are presented as expendable worksheets on which children record their answers.

- Certain Workbook and Textbook pages carry the symbol **H** to refer to Home Link-up. For example, the reference $\boxed{\text{H}^{24}}$ appears on Textbook Page 9 to indicate that homework about that part of the Textbook can be found in activity 24 of Home Link-up.

- Some questions carry a 'Problem solving' flag. For example, this question, involving finding pairs of numbers which add to 92, appears in activity 16.

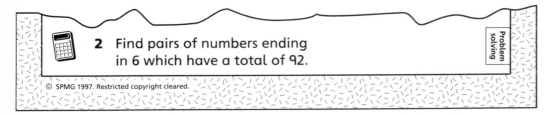

> **2** Find pairs of numbers ending in 6 which have a total of 92.
>
> Problem solving
>
> © SPMG 1997. Restricted copyright cleared.

- This symbol is used to indicate homework activities or specific examples where the use of a calculator is recommended.

Organizing and using the children's material

- It is not intended that children tackle all 60 homework activities. A selection should be made to suit their needs and abilities. A typical activity contains several examples. Teachers can select from the examples to suit individual children.

- The contents list in this booklet and the headings of the activities themselves can be consulted when choosing appropriate homework to match work in schools.

- Some of the activities are of a practical nature and are designed to use materials likely to be available at home. Materials required include counters, cubes or coins to help with number activities, coloured pencils, a ruler, a calculator, mirror, scissors and glue.

- A photocopied page containing two activities can be cut into two parts before issuing one of them to the children or, if issued as a whole page, the children can be instructed to attempt the two activities on different occasions.

- The children may be allowed more than one evening to complete a homework activity.

- Many of the activities use contexts related to those in the Workbooks and Textbook of Heinemann Mathematics 3. The children can be encouraged to explain these contexts to their parents.

- Ideally, the children's homework should be discussed and corrected in school as soon as possible after it has been attempted. Time may be saved by dealing with this in a group situation, correcting and discussing answers to discover who has been experiencing difficulties. An example which has proved difficult for a number of children can be used to revise and reinforce the mathematics underlying it.

- The *Extra* activities are additional work, not necessarily linked to current work in school. They are intended as 'something different' which will be appropriate for children who enjoy such challenges.

Guidance for parents

■ As the title Home Link-up implies, it is important to explain to parents the purpose of the material and how they can help with their children's mathematics at home.

■ *A page of Guidance for Parents is provided on page iv of these notes.* It can be copied and sent to parents when their children start to use Home Link-up. Teachers may also wish to talk to parents about the material when they meet them in school.

■ Parents should certainly be encouraged to talk to their children about the homework they are doing. They should be clear that they are not expected to 'teach' and should not exert undue pressure on a child who is experiencing difficulty with a homework task; rather they should be encouraged to make a brief note on the back of the activity sheet.

Record sheet

■ *A Home Link-up Record Sheet is provided on page v of these notes.* It can be photocopied and attached to the child's homework book.

■ Children should indicate on the sheet when a particular activity has been completed.

Guidance for Parents

Dear Parent,

Heinemann Mathematics: Home Link-up

As we believe that regular homework is a valuable part of your child's education we have adopted Home Link-up to provide extra practice in mathematics. We expect that it will also give you an insight into the work your child does in school.

Each Home Link-up activity should take your child about 15 to 20 minutes to complete. The activities are provided as fill-in sheets. The heading for each activity describes its mathematical content, for example

Heinemann Mathematics 3 Home Link-up Workbook 1, page 10	5
Money to 15p	

A few activities may require materials such as counters, cubes, coins, coloured pencils, a ruler, mirror, scissors or glue.
Where this symbol appears a calculator may be used.

Home Link-up should help foster a positive attitude to mathematics. Working on their own, children can tackle the activities at their own pace, and develop good study habits.

You can help by talking to your child about the work, praising them and offering help where appropriate. Finally, if your child has problems with the work, don't worry! Just reassure them, and make a brief note on the back of the activity sheet.

Thank you for your support and co-operation.

Home Link-up Record Sheet

Name:

Number

Addition, subtraction to 20
| 1 | 2 | 3 | 4 | 5 | 6 |
| 7 | 8 | 9 | 10 | 11 | 12 |

Place value, Addition to 99
| 13 | 14 | 15 | 16 | 17 | 18 | 19 |

Subtraction to 99
| 20 | 21 | 22 | 23 | 24 | 25 |
| 26 | 27 | 28 |

Multiplication
| 29 | 30 | 31 | 32 | 33 | 34 |
| 35 | 36 | 37 | 38 |

Division
| 39 | 40 | 41 |

Fractions
| 42 | 43 | 44 |

Division
| 45 | 46 | 47 |

Measure

Time
| 48 | 49 | 50 | 51 | 52 |

Length
| 53 |

Area
| 54 |

Shape

3D Shape
| 55 |

Tiling, Symmetry
| 56 | 57 | 58 |

Handling data

Handling data
| 59 | 60 |

Heinemann Mathematics 3

v

Use 14 counters, cubes or coins. Make stories for 14.

5 + 9 ———	+ ———	+ ———
+ ———	+ ———	+ ———

☐ + ☐ + ☐ = 14

☐ + ☐ + ☐ = 14

1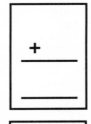

$9 + \boxed{} = 14$ $5 + \boxed{} = 14$

$14 - 5 = \boxed{}$ $14 - 9 = \boxed{}$

2

8 + 6 ———	7 + 7 ———	1 4 − 7 ———	7p + 6p ——— p	1 4p − 4p ———	1 4p − 6p ———

3 How much altogether?

Dodgems 8p + Rocket 6p = _____ p

Boats 9p + Bikes 5p = _____   Lolly 5p + Ice Cream 7p = _____

Name	Heinemann Mathematics 3 Home Link-up Workbook 1, page 6	**3**
	Addition facts for 15	

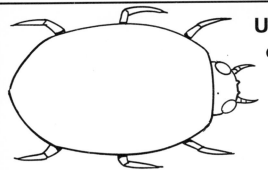 Use 15 counters,
cubes or coins.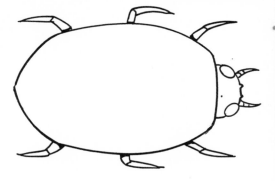

1 Make stories for 15.

9 + 6 ——	+ ——	+ ——	+ ——	+ ——	+ ——	+ ——

2 Tick (✔) each story which is correct.

3 + 7 + 5 = 15   6 + 3 + 6 = 15   7 + 3 + 4 = 15

Name	Heinemann Mathematics 3 Home Link-up Workbook 1, pages 7 and 8	**4**
	Addition and subtraction facts to 15	

1

6 + 9 = _____   15 – 9 = _____

9 + 6 = _____   15 – 6 = _____

2

10 + 5 = _____   15 – 5 = _____

5 + 10 = _____   15 – 10 = _____

3

5 +10 ——	8 + 7 ——	9 + 5 ——	15 – 8 ——	15 – 7 ——	15 –10 ——

4 4 + 6 + 5 = _____   5 + 4 + 5 = _____   7 + 2 + 6 = _____

| 8p | 9p | 7p | 6p | 5p | 7p |

1 Find the total cost of the badges on each bag.

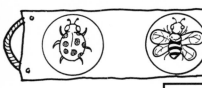  

_____ + _____ = [ ]   _____ + _____ = [ ]   _____ + _____ = [ ]

2 How much is left?

15p – 10p = [ ]   15p – 8p = [ ]   15p – 9p = [ ]

---

1 How many ducks [ ]

swans [ ]

altogether? [ ]

2 Use 16 counters, cubes
or coins.
Find other ways to make 16.

| + | + | + | + |
| 1 6 | | | |

[ ] + [ ] = 16   [ ] + [ ] = 16

[ ] + [ ] + [ ] = 16   [ ] + [ ] + [ ] = 16

1

$7 + 9 =$ _____

$9 + 7 =$ _____

$16 - 9 =$ _____

$16 - 7 =$ _____

2

```
  1 0        8       1 4       1 6
+   6      + 7      -  9      -  8
-----      ----     -----     -----
```

3 $7 + 7 =$ _____ $15 - 6 =$ _____

4 Match each fish to a rod.

 $8 + 8$ $6 + 9$ $14 - 5$  $6 + 8$ $15 - 8$  $16 - 10$

 9    16    14   15    6   7

---

1 Complete.

```
    9        1 8       1 0
 +  8      -   9      +  7
 -----     -----      -----
```

$9 + 9 =$ _____ $8 + 9 =$ _____

```
 1 7
 - 9
-----
```

```
 1 0
 + 8
-----
```

```
 1 8
 - 8
-----
```

```
 1 7
 -1 0
-----
```

```
 1 7
 - 8
-----
```

2 Make 18.

 8 + ☐

 9 + ☐

 9 + ☐ + ☐

roll  8p   milk 9p   banana  7p

I You may use coins. Find the cost and list the coins.

roll	8p	milk		milk	
milk	+ 9p	banana	+ ___	milk	+ ___

altogether ___ p   altogether ___   altogether ___

coins

coins

coins

2 $16 - 9 =$ ____ $18 - 9 =$ ____ $17 - 8 =$ ____

   $17 - 7 =$ ____ $16 - 10 =$ ____ $18 - 8 =$ ____

   $7 + 9 =$ ____ $10 + 7 =$ ____ $8 + 8 =$ ____

I How many squares ____

   triangles ____

   shapes? ____

 How many more circles
are needed to make 17? _____

3

$10 + 7 =$	$6 + 9 =$	$7 + 6 =$
$15 - 6 =$	$20 - 10 =$	$17 - 8 =$

4

$$\begin{array}{cc} 5 \\ + 9 \\ \hline \end{array} \qquad \begin{array}{cc} 1\,8 \\ - 8 \\ \hline \end{array} \qquad \begin{array}{cc} 9 \\ + 8 \\ \hline \end{array} \qquad \begin{array}{cc} 1\,6 \\ - 7 \\ \hline \end{array} \qquad \begin{array}{cc} 1\,0 \\ + 1\,0 \\ \hline \end{array} \qquad \begin{array}{cc} 8 \\ + 7 \\ \hline \end{array}$$

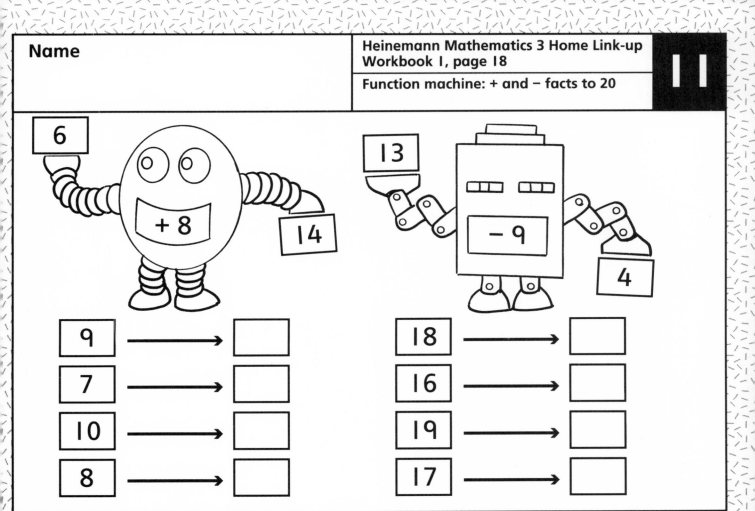

1 Find the racing car numbers.

(a) ☐   (b) ☐   (c) ☐   (d) ☐   (e) ☐   (f) ☐

2 Li spent _____ p

Li

Tim spent _____

Who spent more? _____

How much more? _____

6p

Tim

7p

7p

9p

Tens	Units

30 + 5 ____ = ▢

Tens	Units

____ + ____ = ▢

Tens	Units

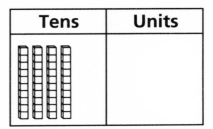

____ + ____ = ▢

Tens	Units

____ + ____ = ▢

Tens	Units

____ + ____ = ▢

Tens	Units

____ + ____ = ▢

There are 23 pencils on the table.
23 is 20 to the nearest ten.

1 Write these numbers to the nearest ten.

24 → ▢   53 → ▢   81 → ▢   12 →

There are 27 brushes on the table.
27 is 30 to the nearest ten.

2 Write these numbers to the nearest ten.

18 → ▢   39 → ▢   66 → ▢   87 → ▢

1 Complete to see a pattern.

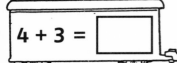

4 + 3 = ☐   14 + 3 = ☐   24 + 3 = ☐   34 + 3 = ☐

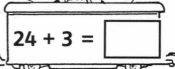

2 73 + 6 = ☐   5 + 84 = ☐   42 + 5 = ☐   8 + 90 = ☐

3 Complete to see a pattern.

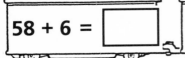

58 + 6 = ☐   68 + 6 = ☐   78 + 6 = ☐   88 + 6 = ☐

4

```
   3 6        7       2 9        2       4 7       6 1
 +   5      + 5 8    +   9     + 6 8    +   7     +   9
 ─────      ─────    ─────     ─────    ─────     ─────
```

```
  1 6   flower cards
+ 3 3   animal cards
─────
  4 9   cards altogether.
```

1

```
  4 2               2 5               3 6               1 7
+ 1 3             + 6 4             + 4 0             + 8 2
─────             ─────             ─────             ─────
```

```
  5 3        2 8        5 4        4 9        4 8        3 9
+ 3 8      + 6 5      + 1 6      + 2 7      + 4 8      + 5 1
─────      ─────      ─────      ─────      ─────      ─────
```

**2 Find pairs of numbers ending
in 6 which have a total of 92.**

Problem solving

1 Find the totals.

```
  3 7        4 2        3 6        2 5
+ 2 5      + 1 8      + 2 7      + 4 5
-----      -----      -----      -----
```

Add, sum, total

2 How much is
60p plus 38p?   + ____

____

3 Find the sum
of 56 and 27.   + ____

____

4 Find each total.

```
  5 0        3 6        4 6
  1 4        2 9          9
+ 2 5      + 1 3      + 1 8
-----      -----      -----
```

Extra

■ Find five pairs of **odd** numbers that add to 18.

■ Find five pairs of odd numbers **greater than 20** that add to 58.

1 List coins to buy

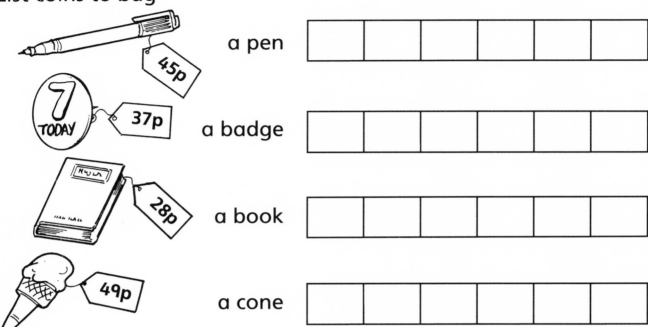

a pen

a badge

a book

a cone

2 How much money has each child?

 Tom   ⬚ p

 Mark  ⬚ p

 Emma  ⬚ p

3 Emma spent 50p. How much had she left? _____

Name	Heinemann Mathematics 3 Home Link-up Workbook 1, pages 29 and 30 Money to 99p	19

Ben bought a burger. He used these coins.

68p				
50p	10p	5p	2p	1p	

1 List coins to buy:

chips 57p						
cake 75p						
toastie 83p						
potato 94p						

2 How much money has each child?

Lisa

[ ] p altogether

Ben

[ ] altogether

1   $9 - 6 =$ ☐ $19 - 6 =$ ☐ $29 - 6 =$ ☐

    $9 - 4 =$ ☐ $19 - 4 =$ ☐ $29 - 4 =$ ☐

28 children in the café.
 5 came out.
23 were left.

$$\begin{array}{r} 2\,8 \\ -\ 5 \\ \hline 2\,3 \\ \hline \end{array}$$

2

$$\begin{array}{r} 3\,6 \\ -\ 4 \\ \hline \end{array}$$
$$\begin{array}{r} 4\,9 \\ -\ 8 \\ \hline \end{array}$$
$$\begin{array}{r} 6\,7 \\ -\ 1 \\ \hline \end{array}$$

$59 - 7 =$ ☐ $64 - 2 =$ ☐

$48 - 3 =$ ☐ $88 - 8 =$ ☐

---

68 children in the school hall.
23 children go to their classroom.
45 were left.

$$\begin{array}{r} 6\,8 \\ -2\,3 \\ \hline 4\,5 \\ \hline \end{array}$$

1   $$\begin{array}{r} 3\,7 \\ -1\,6 \\ \hline \end{array}$$
$$\begin{array}{r} 8\,5 \\ -2\,2 \\ \hline \end{array}$$
$$\begin{array}{r} 6\,9 \\ -3\,7 \\ \hline \end{array}$$
$$\begin{array}{r} 4\,8 \\ -3\,0 \\ \hline \end{array}$$
$$\begin{array}{r} 7\,5 \\ -3\,5 \\ \hline \end{array}$$

2   Each child has to
    stack 48 chairs.
    How many chairs has
    each still to stack?

 31 stacked

 26 stacked

 44 stacked

$$\begin{array}{r} 4\,8 \\ -3\,1 \\ \hline \end{array}$$

$$\begin{array}{r} 4\,8 \\ - \\ \hline \end{array}$$

$$\begin{array}{r} \\ - \\ \hline \end{array}$$

1 Complete each row to see a pattern.

13 – 6 = ☐   23 – 6 = ☐   33 – 6 = ☐   43 – 6 = ☐

15 – 7 = ☐   25 – 7 = ☐   35 – 7 = ☐   45 – 7 = ☐

2 How many strawberries does each child have left?

```
  3 2
-   5
------
```

```
  5 4
-   8
------
```
```
  8 1
-   7
------
```

```
  6 0
-   4
------
```

1
```
  4 3        8 4        7 0        9 2        6 1        7 6
- 1 6      - 2 9      - 3 7      - 4 5      - 2 3      - 4 8
------     ------     ------     ------     ------     ------
```

2 How many more raspberries has Bob?

```
  5 3
- 2 7
```
53   27   _____

```
  5 3
- 1 9
```
53   19   _____

```
  5 3
- 3 5
```
53   35   _____

3 Kim picks 81 strawberries.   8 1

   She eats 27.   – _____

   How many are left?   _____

1 81 take away 27.   **2** 61 subtract 16   **3** Find the difference between 23 and 72.

4    Jean scored 37. How many more does she need to score 50?

5

77	83	97	66	71	80
−37	−46	−60	−29	−34	−18
____	____	____	____	____	____

Each child had a 20p coin to spend.
Use coins to count out the change. Check.

Raj bought   **Change**

Check
20p
−7p
⬚ p   ____ p

Vera bought   **Change**

Check
20
−14
⬚ p   ____ p

Sara bought   **Change**

Check
20p
−9p
⬚ p   ____ p

Each child had a 50p coin to spend.
Use coins to count out the change. Check.

David bought   **Change**   **Check**   5 0p

 38p      − 3 8p

☐ p   p

Liam bought   **Change**   **Check**   5 0p

  26p   ☐   −

Diana bought   **Change**   **Check**   5 0p

17p   ☐   −

 55p **Magic Mirrors**   **Spooky Stories** 18p   26p **Haunted Horrors**

1 Which is dearest? _____

Which is cheapest? _____

Find the difference in price. _____

2 What is the total cost
of the three tickets? _____

_____

3 Zara had 90p.
She went to the Magic Mirrors and the Spooky Stories.   _____
How much did she have left?   _____

1 How many children are on each bus?

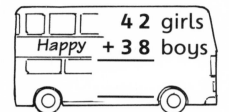
Happy   **4 2** girls
       + 3 8 boys

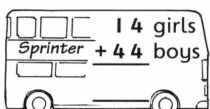
Sprinter **1 4** girls
       + 4 4 boys

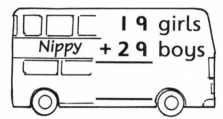
Nippy   **1 9** girls
       + 2 9 boys

2
How many more
children are on
Sprinter than
Nippy?

3
Find the difference
between the numbers
of girls on Happy and
Sprinter.

4 63 + 36 = 99   27 + 72 = 99

Write other pairs of numbers
like these which total 99.

Problem solving

Extra

Tick (✔) the squares which are magic.

23	19	39
43	27	11
15	35	31

26	20	24
21	23	25
22	26	20

29	36	31
34	32	30
33	28	35

1 Complete.

___ times ___

___ × ___

___ times ___

___ × ___

___ times ___

___ × ___

___ times ___

___ × ___

2 Draw 4×3 fish.

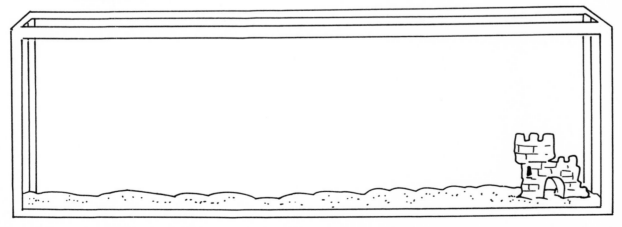

1

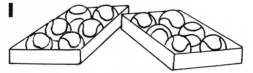    

2 × 6 = ☐   2 × 4 = ☐   2 × 10 = ☐

2 × 7 = ☐   2 × 3 = ☐   2 × 8 = ☐

2 × 2 = ☐   2 × 9 = ☐   2 × 0 = ☐

2

2 fives → 10

2 ones → ◯

2 eights → ◯

2 nines → ◯

2 fours → ◯

2 tens → ◯

3 Match.

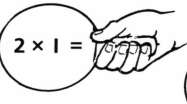 2 × 1 =

2 sevens

  2 × 5

2 sixes

⑩   ②   ⑭   ⑫

4 Write the missing numbers.

② ④ ⑥ ◯ ◯ ⑫ ◯ ◯ ⑳

1 Three trays. 4 ants in each.

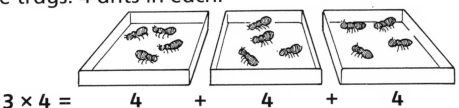

$3 \times 4 =$ 4   +   4   +   4   = ____

2

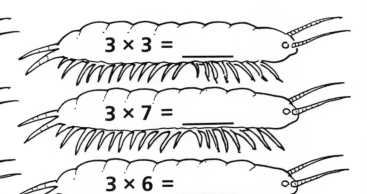

$3 \times 1 =$ ____

$3 \times 0 =$ ____

$3 \times 10 =$ ____

$3 \times 3 =$ ____

$3 \times 7 =$ ____

$3 \times 6 =$ ____

3 Colour to match.

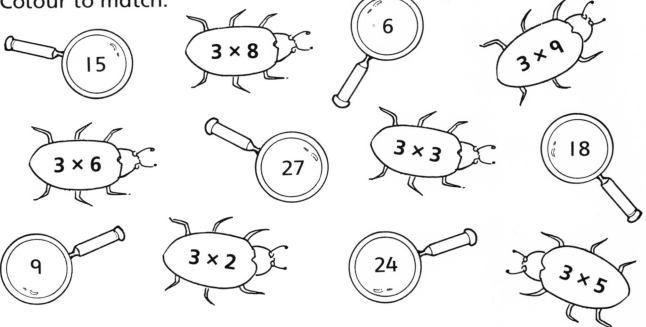

15   3×8 6 3×9

3×6 27 3×3 18

9   3×2 24 3×5

4 Complete the number pattern.

3   6   __   12   __   18   __   __   27

1 How many paints are there on

    2 square trays? ____

    3 round trays? ____

    3 square trays **and** 2 round trays? ____

2 How many pencils are there in

    2 boxes ____   3 boxes? ____

3 How many paints are there in

    2 boxes ____   3 boxes? ____

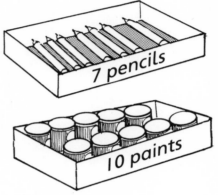

7 pencils

10 paints

---

1 Find the cost of

    2 biscuits   _____

    3 cakes   _____

    3 apples   _____

    2 pieces of orange   _____

    2 carrots _____   3 biscuits _____

    3 pieces of orange and 1 carrot _____

    2 apples and 3 carrots _____

6p 7p 4p 9p 8p

2 Sharon had 20 pence.
She bought 2 cakes.
What was her change? _____

3 Mark had 20 pence.
He bought 2 carrots.
What was his change? _____

Name	Heinemann Mathematics 3 Home Link-up Workbook 2, page 12	**34**
	Multiplication: using the 4 times table	

1

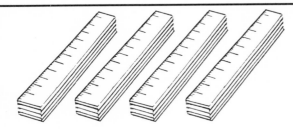

4 × 4 = _____ rulers

4 × 8 = _____ paintbrushes

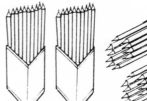

4 × 10 = _____ pencils

2

4 × 1p = _____ p   4 × 2p = _____   4 × 5p = _____

4 × 8p = _____ p   4 × 7p = _____   4 × 9p = _____

3   Colour to match.

 4 × 6   4 × 3   28   0   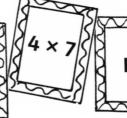 4 × 7   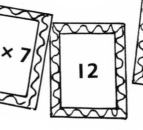 12   24    4 × 0

4   Write the missing numbers.

4	8	12			24		32	

5   4 × 9 = ☐   4 × 0 = ☐   4 × 3 = ☐

4 × ☐ = 24   4 × ☐ = 28   4 × ☐ = 20

© SPMG 1997. Restricted copyright cleared.

1 Colour to match.

5 × 7   30   5 × 5   5 × 6   35   5 × 0

25   5 × 1   0   5 × 3   5   15

2

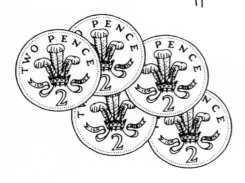

5 × 2p = _____ p   5 × 5p = _____   5 × 10p = _____

5 × 3p = _____ p   5 × 7p = _____   5 × 9p = _____

3 Join the numbers in order.

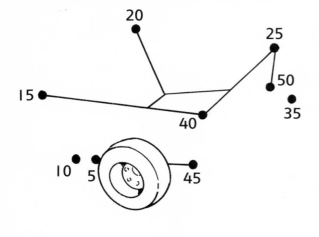

20   25   • 30
50
15•   35
40
10 5   45

4 Complete.

5 × 4 = ☐

5 × ☐ = 40

5 × ☐ = 0

5 Write the missing numbers.

5   10   15   ___   ___   30   35   ___   ___   50

 5 carrots  7 potatoes 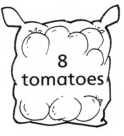 8 tomatoes  6 onions

1 How many?

carrots in 4 bags _____   potatoes in 5 bags _____

onions in 4 bags _____   tomatoes in 5 bags _____

potatoes in 4 bags _____   onions in 5 bags _____

tomatoes in 4 bags _____   carrots in 5 bags _____

2

20 turnips altogether.

$4 \times$ _____ $= 20$

3 $5 \times$ _____ $= 50$

$4 \times$ _____ $= 36$

$5 \times$ _____ $= 5$

4   Prices    9p   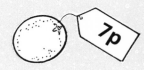 7p    4p

4 apples cost   5 oranges cost

5 pears cost _____   4 pears   cost _____

Total cost _____ p   Total cost _____ p

1 Write each answer.

2 × 7

4 × 8

3 × 9

5 × 5

3 × 3

10 × 2

5 × 7

4 × 6

2 Colour the **even** answers red and the **odd** answers blue.

---

1 How many of each does Sarah have?

2 boxes with 8 vans in each. _____ vans

4 boxes with 5 trucks in each. _____ trucks

5 boxes with 9 cars in each. _____ cars

2 Find the cost of

3 dog stickers _____

2 car stickers _____

4 football stickers _____

10 dog stickers _____

5 football stickers and a car sticker. _____

Use cubes, counters or coins.

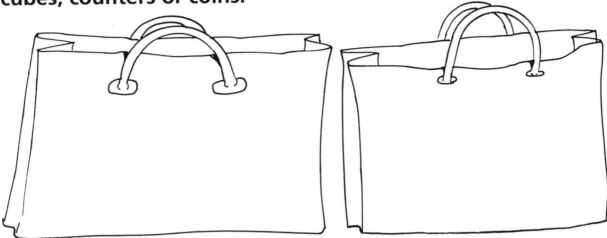

1 Share equally between the 2 bags.

8 tins

How many tins in each bag? _____

12 tubs

How many tubs in each bag? _____

18 packets

How many packets in each bag? _____

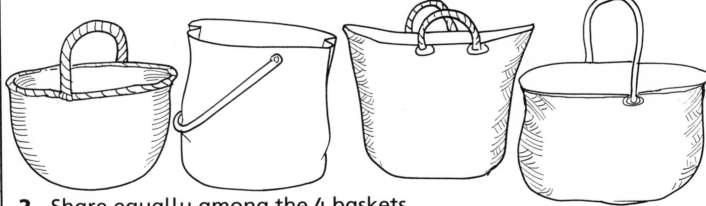

2 Share equally among the 4 baskets

8 apples

How many apples in each basket? _____

20 sweets

How many sweets in each basket? _____

16 eggs

How many eggs in each basket? _____

Use cubes, counters or coins.

1 Share equally among 3 boats.

6 ÷ 3 =		12 ÷ 3 =		15 ÷ 3 =	

18 ÷ 3 =		9 ÷ 3 =		24 ÷ 3 =	

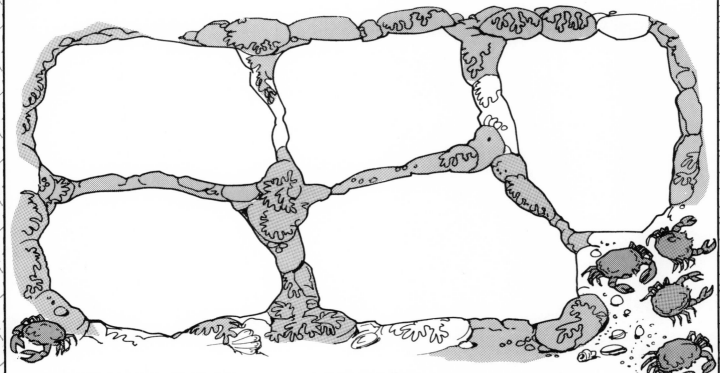

2 Share crabs equally among 5 pools.

5 ÷ 5 = ____   20 ÷ 5 = ____   25 ÷ 5 = ____

10 ÷ 5 = ____   15 ÷ 5 = ____   30 ÷ 5 = ____

Use cubes, counters or coins.

1  Share 9 books equally among 4 children.

How many books for each child? ____

How many left over? ____

$$9 \div 4 = \underline{\quad} \ r \ \underline{\quad}$$

2 $7 \div 2 = \underline{\quad} \ r \ \underline{\quad}$ $18 \div 4 = \underline{\quad} \ r \ \underline{\quad}$

  $14 \div 3 = \underline{\quad} \ r \ \underline{\quad}$ $9 \div 2 = \underline{\quad} \ r \ \underline{\quad}$

  $13 \div 5 = \underline{\qquad\qquad}$ $11 \div 4 = \underline{\qquad\qquad}$

3 Tick (✔) if the remainder is 2.

| $8 \div 3$ | $15 \div 5$ | $9 \div 5$ | $10 \div 4$ | $12 \div 5$ |

 Colour $\frac{3}{4}$ 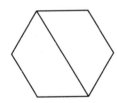 Colour $\frac{2}{2}$ 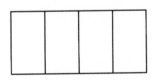 Colour $\frac{1}{4}$  Colour $\frac{2}{4}$

2 What fraction of each shape is shaded?

   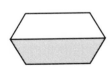   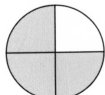   

____   ____   ____   ____

1 Colour $\frac{1}{2}$ of the cubes.

$\frac{1}{2}$ of ____ = ____

2 Colour $\frac{1}{2}$ of the cubes.

$\frac{1}{2}$ of ____ = ____

Use cubes, coins or counters.

3 $\frac{1}{2}$ of 12 = ____ $\frac{1}{2}$ of 18 = ____ $\frac{1}{2}$ of 10 = ____ $\frac{1}{2}$ of 14 = ____

4 Tom had 16 sweets. He gave half of them to Sue.
How many did he give to Sue? _____

1 Colour $\frac{1}{4}$ of the biscuits.

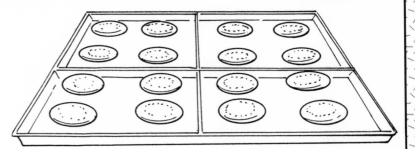

$\frac{1}{4}$ of ____ = ____

Use cubes, coins or counters.

2 $\frac{1}{4}$ of 24 = ____ $\frac{1}{4}$ of 32 = ____

$\frac{1}{4}$ of 40 = ____ $\frac{1}{4}$ of 20 = ____

3 Sal had 36 cakes.
She gave one quarter to Jake.
How many did she give to Jake? ____

1 There are 10 children. How many groups of 2? ___

Use counters, cubes or coins.

2 15 children. How many groups of 3? ___

How many groups of 5? ___

3 20 children. How many groups of 5? ___

How many groups of 4? ___

How many groups of 2? ___

1 Ring groups of 4. $12 \div 4 =$ ___

2 Use cubes, counters or coins.

$6 \div 2 =$ ___ $8 \div 4 =$ ___ $15 \div 5 =$ ___

$9 \div 3 =$ ___ $10 \div 5 =$ ___ $8 \div 2 =$ ___

$12 \div 3 =$ ___ $16 \div 4 =$ ___ $18 \div 3 =$ ___

Name	Heinemann Mathematics 3 Home Link-up Workbook 2, page 38	**47**
	Division: grouping with remainders	

1

How many flowers? ____

How many groups of 3? ____

How many left over? ____

10 ÷ 3 = ____ r ____

Use cubes, counters or coins.

2 13 ÷ 4 = ____ r ____   12 ÷ 5 = ____ r ____

  7 ÷ 2 = ____ r ____   11 ÷ 3 = ____ r ____

  14 ÷ 5 = _____   15 ÷ 4 = _____

Name	Heinemann Mathematics 3 Home Link-up MSHD Workbook, page 4	**48**
	Time: interpreting digital times	

1 Write each take-off time.

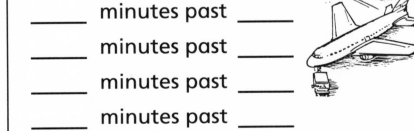

'Plane to	Take-off time	
Aberdeen	10:25	____ minutes past ____
Belfast	10:50	____ minutes past ____
Cardiff	11:04	____ minutes past ____
Dublin	11:30	____ minutes past ____
Leeds	12:59	____ minutes past ____

2 Which plane takes off at half past eleven? _____

3 The Leeds plane took off one minute **after** 12:59. When did it take off?

☐ : ☐

Fit for Life ♥

The Fun Run started at 3 o'clock.

Zara stopped running after <u>20</u> minutes.
The time was
<u>20</u> minutes past <u>3</u> .

1 The clocks show when some other children stopped running. Write their times.

Mike stopped running after

_____ minutes.

Time:

_____ minutes past _____ .

Tracey stopped running after

_____ minutes.

Time:

_____ minutes past _____ .

2 Write the start times for these clubs.

Badminton

_____ minutes past _____

Chess

_____ minutes past _____

Art

_____ minutes past _____

Music

_____ minutes past _____

Write the digital time for each clock.

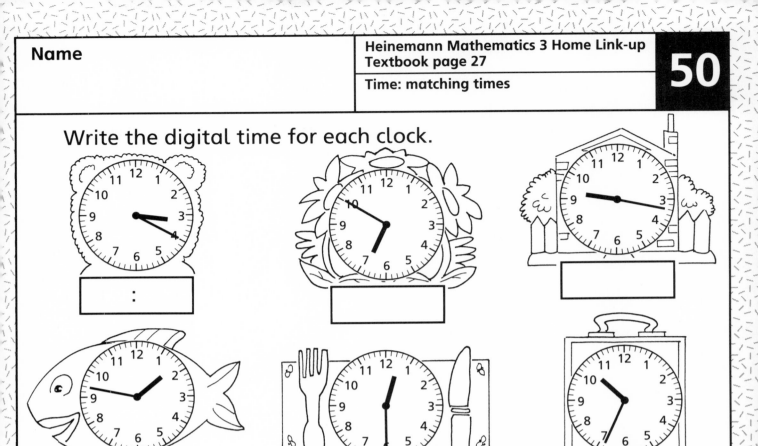

Write each time: Use **quarter past** or **quarter to**.

1 Write the **before** and **after** times.

One hour before	Time	One hour after
half past 2	(clock showing 2:45)	
	7:15	

One hour before	Time	One hour after
	4:45	
	(clock showing 12:00)	

2 Find how long each journey took.

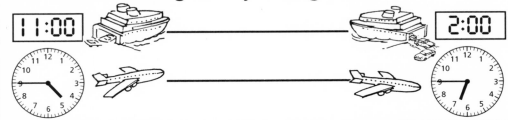

Extra

Use a tape which is marked in centimetres.

Measure in centimetres. Ask an adult to check.

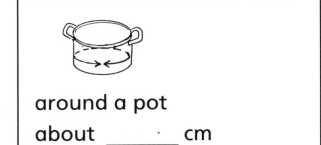

around a pot

about _____ cm

height of a chair

about _____ cm

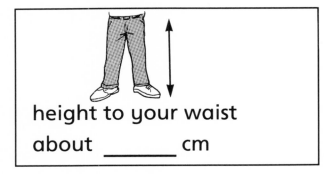

height to your waist

about _____ cm

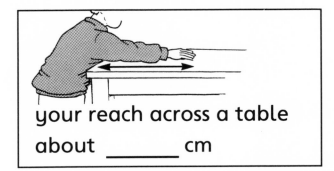

your reach across a table

about _____ cm

1 Estimate, then measure in centimetres, the height of each flower.

Estimate _____
Measure _____

Estimate _____
Measure _____

Estimate _____
Measure _____

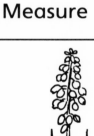

Estimate _____
Measure _____

Estimate _____
Measure _____

Estimate _____
Measure _____

2 Measure these lengths in centimetres.

the bee _____   the longest leaf _____

3 Draw a butterfly 5 cm wide.

4 Measure this sheet.

length about _____ cm

width about _____ cm

1 Write the area of each letter.

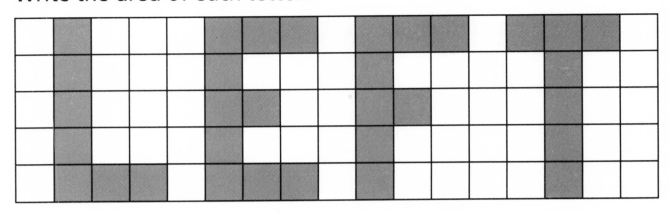

_____ squares   _____ squares   _____ squares   _____ squares

2 What is the area of this shape?

_____ squares

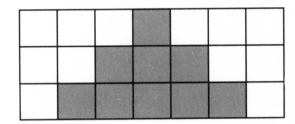

Draw a shape with a **smaller** area. Colour it blue.
Draw a shape with a **larger** area.   Colour it red.

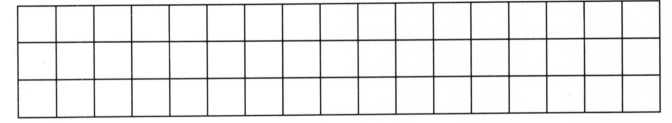

3 Draw and colour 3 **different** shapes each with an area of 9 squares.

Name	Heinemann Mathematics 3 Home Link-up MSHD Workbook, page 21	**55**
	3D Shape: triangular prisms	

1 (a) Colour to sort the shapes.

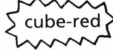  cone - blue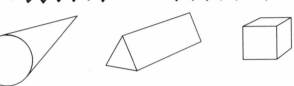

(b) Tick (✔) the name for the shapes that are **not** coloured.

spheres   triangles   squares   triangular prisms

2 Colour.

triangular prisms blue	pyramids red	spheres green

  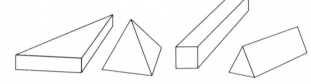   

Name	Heinemann Mathematics 3 Home Link-up MSHD Workbook, pages 25 and 26	**56**
	Tiling	

Complete by drawing more squares **and** rectangles.
Use 2 colours to make a pattern.

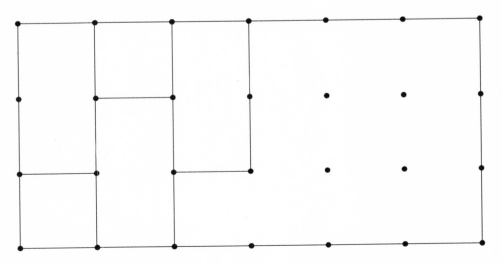

1 Shade to make the pattern symmetrical.

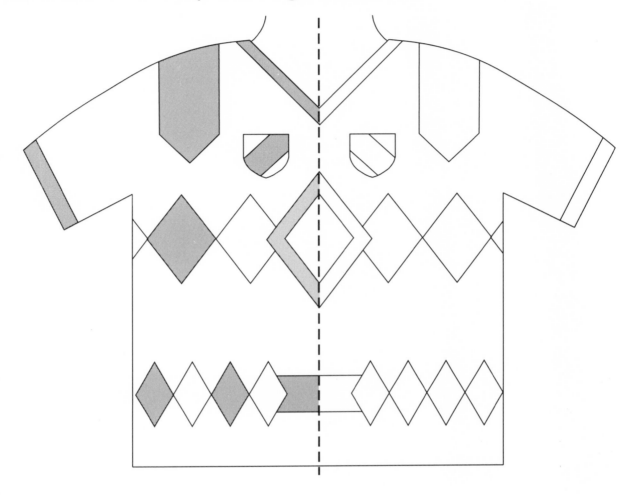

2 Cut out the shapes below.
Fold each and mark any line of symmetry.
Stick the shapes on the back of this sheet.

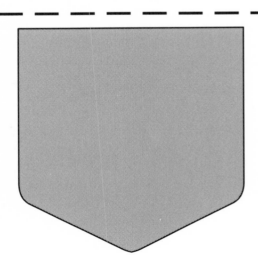

Use a mirror if you wish.

I Draw a line of symmetry on each.

2 Colour the squares to make a symmetrical pattern.

	red		blue	red	red
blue			red		
- - -	- - -	- - -	- - -	- - -	- - -
	red	red		red	blue
red		red			

On the school trip the children bought these things in Sam's café.

red group

blue group

green group

yellow group

1 Use the tick sheet to count what they bought.

2 Make a graph of your results.

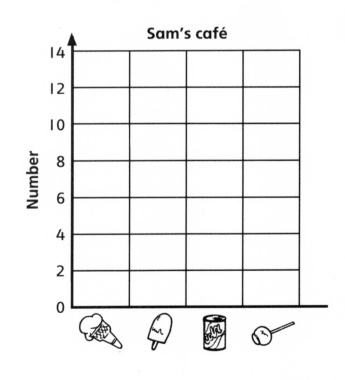

red group				
blue group				
green group				
yellow group				
Total				

3 What did Sam sell most of _____   fewest of ? _____

4 Which **group** bought the greatest number of things? _____

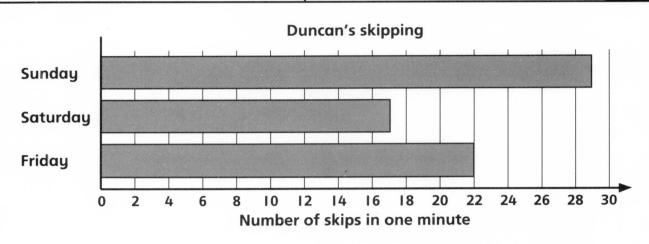

1 (a) What is the total number of skips on Friday and Saturday? _____ _____

(b) Find the difference between the number of skips on Friday and Sunday. _____ _____

2 (a) Complete the graph of Duncan's skips for the rest of the week.

Monday	18 skips		Tuesday	13 skips		Wednesday	7 skips		Thursday	15 skips

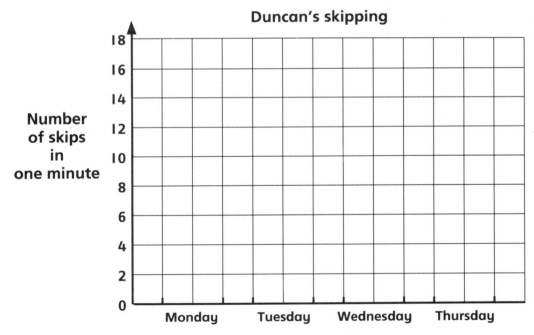

(b) Write a sentence about your graph. _____

_____

Answers

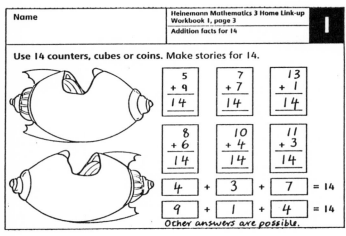

1 Heinemann Mathematics 3 Home Link-up
Workbook 1, page 3
Addition facts for 14

Use 14 counters, cubes or coins. Make stories for 14.

5	7	13
+ 9	+ 7	+ 1
14	14	14

8	10	11
+ 6	+ 4	+ 3
14	14	14

$\boxed{4} + \boxed{3} + \boxed{7} = 14$

$\boxed{9} + \boxed{1} + \boxed{4} = 14$

Other answers are possible.

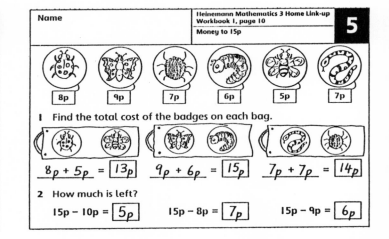

5 Heinemann Mathematics 3 Home Link-up
Workbook 1, page 10
Money to 15p

8p   9p   7p   6p   5p   7p

1 Find the total cost of the badges on each bag.

$8p + 5p = \boxed{13p}$ $9p + 6p = \boxed{15p}$ $7p + 7p = \boxed{14p}$

2 How much is left?

$15p - 10p = \boxed{5p}$ $15p - 8p = \boxed{7p}$ $15p - 9p = \boxed{6p}$

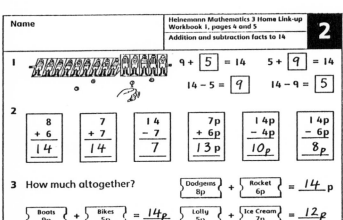

2 Heinemann Mathematics 3 Home Link-up
Workbook 1, pages 4 and 5
Addition and subtraction facts to 14

1 $9 + \boxed{5} = 14$ $5 + \boxed{9} = 14$

$14 - 5 = \boxed{9}$ $14 - 9 = \boxed{5}$

2

8	7	14	7p	14p	14p
+ 6	+ 7	− 7	+ 6p	− 4p	− 6p
14	14	7	13p	10p	8p

3 How much altogether?

Dodgems 8p + Rocket 6p = 14 p

Boats 9p + Bikes 5p = 14p   Lolly 5p + Ice Cream 7p = 12p

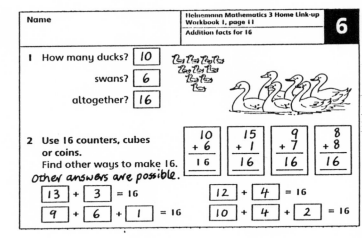

6 Heinemann Mathematics 3 Home Link-up
Workbook 1, page 11
Addition facts for 16

1 How many ducks? 10
swans? 6
altogether? 16

2 Use 16 counters, cubes or coins.
Find other ways to make 16.
Other answers are possible.

10	15	9	8
+ 6	+ 1	+ 7	+ 8
16	16	16	16

$\boxed{13} + \boxed{3} = 16$ $\boxed{12} + \boxed{4} = 16$

$\boxed{9} + \boxed{6} + \boxed{1} = 16$ $\boxed{10} + \boxed{4} + \boxed{2} = 16$

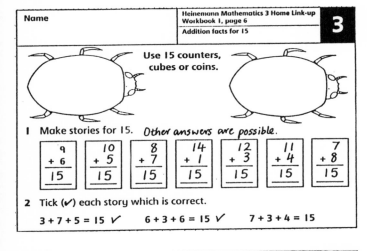

3 Heinemann Mathematics 3 Home Link-up
Workbook 1, page 6
Addition facts for 15

Use 15 counters, cubes or coins.

1 Make stories for 15. *Other answers are possible.*

9	10	8	14	12	11	7
+ 6	+ 5	+ 7	+ 1	+ 3	+ 4	+ 8
15	15	15	15	15	15	15

2 Tick (✔) each story which is correct.

$3 + 7 + 5 = 15$ ✔ $6 + 3 + 6 = 15$ ✔ $7 + 3 + 4 = 15$

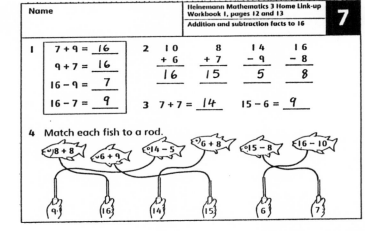

7 Heinemann Mathematics 3 Home Link-up
Workbook 1, pages 12 and 13
Addition and subtraction facts to 16

1

$7 + 9 = \underline{16}$
$9 + 7 = \underline{16}$
$16 - 9 = \underline{7}$
$16 - 7 = \underline{9}$

2

10	8	14	16
+ 6	+ 7	− 9	− 8
16	15	5	8

3 $7 + 7 = \underline{14}$ $15 - 6 = \underline{9}$

4 Match each fish to a rod.

8 + 8   6 + 9   14 − 5   6 + 8   15 − 8   16 − 10

9   16   14   15   6   7

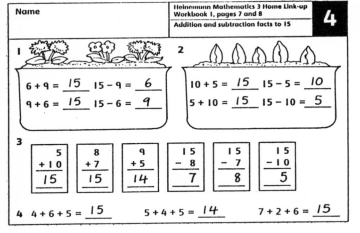

4 Heinemann Mathematics 3 Home Link-up
Workbook 1, pages 7 and 8
Addition and subtraction facts to 15

1
$6 + 9 = \underline{15}$ $15 - 9 = \underline{6}$
$9 + 6 = \underline{15}$ $15 - 6 = \underline{9}$

2
$10 + 5 = \underline{15}$ $15 - 5 = \underline{10}$
$5 + 10 = \underline{15}$ $15 - 10 = \underline{5}$

3

5	8	9	15	15	15
+ 10	+ 7	+ 5	− 8	− 7	− 10
15	15	14	7	8	5

4 $4 + 6 + 5 = \underline{15}$ $5 + 4 + 5 = \underline{14}$ $7 + 2 + 6 = \underline{15}$

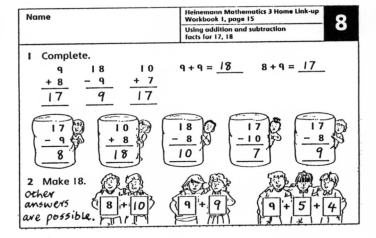

8 Heinemann Mathematics 3 Home Link-up
Workbook 1, page 15
Using addition and subtraction
facts for 17, 18

1 Complete.

9	18	10
+ 8	− 9	+ 7
17	9	17

$9 + 9 = \underline{18}$ $8 + 9 = \underline{17}$

17	10	18	17	17
− 9	+ 8	− 8	− 10	− 8
8	18	10	7	9

2 Make 18.
Other answers are possible.

$\boxed{8} + \boxed{10}$ $\boxed{9} + \boxed{9}$ $\boxed{9} + \boxed{5} + \boxed{4}$

Name

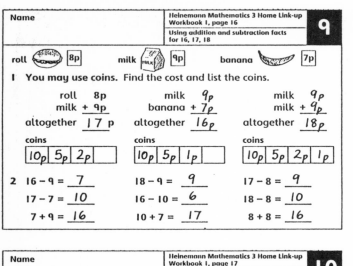

roll [8p] milk [9p] banana [7p]

1 You may use coins. Find the cost and list the coins.

roll 8p	milk 9p	milk 9p
milk + 9p	banana + 7p	milk + 9p
altogether 17 p	altogether 16p	altogether 18p

coins

| 10p | 5p | 2p | | | 10p | 5p | 1p | | | 10p | 5p | 2p | 1p |

2
16 − 9 = 7	18 − 9 = 9	17 − 8 = 9
17 − 7 = 10	16 − 10 = 6	18 − 8 = 10
7 + 9 = 16	10 + 7 = 17	8 + 8 = 16

Name

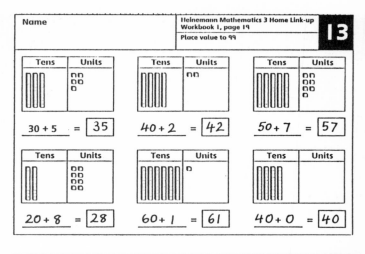

| Tens | Units |
30 + 5 = [35]

| Tens | Units |
40 + 2 = [42]

| Tens | Units |
50 + 7 = [57]

| Tens | Units |
20 + 8 = [28]

| Tens | Units |
60 + 1 = [61]

| Tens | Units |
40 + 0 = [40]

Name

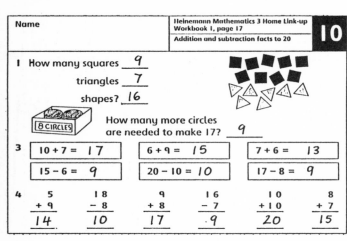

1 How many squares 9
        triangles 7
        shapes? 16

How many more circles
are needed to make 17? 9

3
| 10 + 7 = 17 | 6 + 9 = 15 | 7 + 6 = 13 |
| 15 − 6 = 9 | 20 − 10 = 10 | 17 − 8 = 9 |

4
5	18	9	16	10	8
+ 9	− 8	+ 8	− 7	+ 10	+ 7
14	10	17	9	20	15

Name

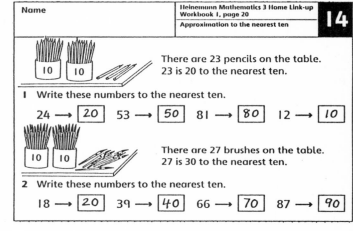

There are 23 pencils on the table.
23 is 20 to the nearest ten.

1 Write these numbers to the nearest ten.

24 → [20] 53 → [50] 81 → [80] 12 → [10]

There are 27 brushes on the table.
27 is 30 to the nearest ten.

2 Write these numbers to the nearest ten.

18 → [20] 39 → [40] 66 → [70] 87 → [90]

Name

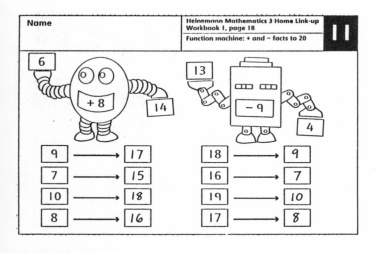

[6] + 8 [14]

[13] − 9 [4]

9 → 17	18 → 9
7 → 15	16 → 7
10 → 18	19 → 10
8 → 16	17 → 8

Heinemann Mathematics 3 Home Link-up
Workbook-1, pages 21 and 22
Adding Units to Tens and Units
15

Name

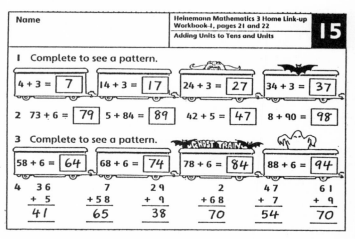

1 Complete to see a pattern.

| 4 + 3 = 7 | 14 + 3 = 17 | 24 + 3 = 27 | 34 + 3 = 37 |

2 73 + 6 = [79] 5 + 84 = [89] 42 + 5 = [47] 8 + 90 = [98]

3 Complete to see a pattern.

| 58 + 6 = 64 | 68 + 6 = 74 | 78 + 6 = 84 | 88 + 6 = 94 |

4
36	7	29	2	47	61
+ 5	+ 58	+ 9	+ 68	+ 7	+ 9
41	65	38	70	54	70

Name

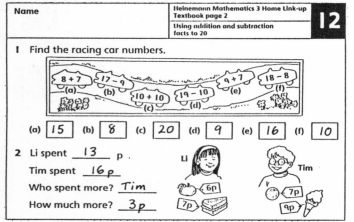

1 Find the racing car numbers.

8 + 7 (a) 17 − 9 (b) 10 + 10 (c) 19 − 10 (d) 9 + 7 (e) 18 − 8 (f)

(a) [15] (b) [8] (c) [20] (d) [9] (e) [16] (f) [10]

2 Li spent 13 p.
Tim spent 16 p
Who spent more? Tim
How much more? 3p

Name

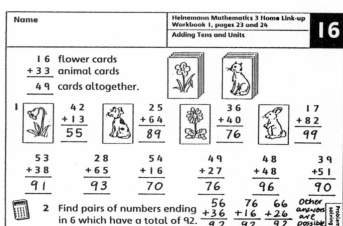

  16 flower cards
+ 33 animal cards
  49 cards altogether.

1
42	25	36	17
+ 13	+ 64	+ 40	+ 82
55	89	76	99

53	28	54	49	48	39
+ 38	+ 65	+ 16	+ 27	+ 48	+ 51
91	93	70	76	96	90

2 Find pairs of numbers ending in 6 which have a total of 92.

56	76	66	Other answers
+ 36	+ 16	+ 26	are possible
92	92	92	

Problem solving

1 Find the totals.

```
  37      42      36      25
+ 25    + 18    + 27    + 45
----    ----    ----    ----
  62      60      63      70
```

Add, sum, total

2 How much is 60p plus 38p?
```
  60p
+ 38p
-----
  98p
```

3 Find the sum of 56 and 27.
```
  56
+ 27
----
  83
```

4 Find each total.
```
  50      36      46
  14      29       9
+ 25    + 13    + 18
----    ----    ----
  89      78      73
```

Extra

■ Find five pairs of **odd** numbers that add to 18.

9 and 9, 15 and 3, 13 and 5, 11 and 7, 1 and 17

■ Find five pairs of odd numbers greater than 20 that add to 58.

23 and 35, 21 and 37, 29 and 29, 31 and 27, 33 and 25

---

1 List coins to buy:

a pen | 20p | 20p | 5p | | |

a badge | 20p | 10p | 5p | 2p | |

a book | 20p | 5p | 2p | 1p | |

a cone | 20p | 20p | 5p | 2p | 2p |

Other answers are possible.

2 How much money has each child?

Tom  75 p

Mark — 83 p

Emma — 91 p

3 Emma spent 50p. How much had she left? 41p

Ben bought a burger. 68p
He used these coins.

1 List coins to buy: | 50p | 10p | 5p | 2p | 1p | |

 chips 57p | 50p | 5p | 2p | | |

cake 75p | 50p | 20p | 5p | | |

toastie 83p | 50p | 20p | 10p | 2p | 1p |

potato 94p | 50p | 20p | 20p | 2p | 2p |

Other answers are possible.

2 How much money has each child?

Lisa

85 p altogether

Ben

99 p altogether

1
$9 - 6 = 3$ $19 - 6 = 13$ $29 - 6 = 23$

$9 - 4 = 5$ $19 - 4 = 15$ $29 - 4 = 25$

28 children in the café.
5 came out.
23 were left.
```
  28
-  5
----
  23
```

2
```
  36      49      67
-  4     - 8     - 1
----    ----    ----
  32      41      66
```

$59 - 7 = 52$ $64 - 2 = 62$

$48 - 3 = 45$ $88 - 8 = 80$

---

68 children in the school hall.
23 children go to their classroom.
45 were left.
```
  68
- 23
----
  45
```

1
```
  37      85      69      48      75
- 16    - 22    - 37    - 30    - 35
----    ----    ----    ----    ----
  21      63      32      18      40
```

2 Each child has to stack 48 chairs. How many chairs has each still to stack?

31 stacked
```
  48
- 31
----
  17
```

26 stacked
```
  48
- 26
----
  22
```

44 stacked
```
  48
- 44
----
   4
```

1 Complete each row to see a pattern.

$13 - 6 = \boxed{7}$ $23 - 6 = \boxed{17}$ $33 - 6 = \boxed{27}$ $43 - 6 = \boxed{37}$

$15 - 7 = \boxed{8}$ $25 - 7 = \boxed{18}$ $35 - 7 = \boxed{28}$ $45 - 7 = \boxed{38}$

2 How many strawberries does each child have left?

$\begin{array}{r}3\,2\\-\ 5\\\hline 27\end{array}$	$\begin{array}{r}5\,4\\-\ 8\\\hline 46\end{array}$	$\begin{array}{r}8\,1\\-\ 7\\\hline 74\end{array}$	$\begin{array}{r}6\,0\\-\ 4\\\hline 56\end{array}$

1

$\begin{array}{r}4\,3\\-1\,6\\\hline 27\end{array}$	$\begin{array}{r}8\,4\\-2\,9\\\hline 55\end{array}$	$\begin{array}{r}7\,0\\-3\,7\\\hline 33\end{array}$	$\begin{array}{r}9\,2\\-4\,5\\\hline 47\end{array}$	$\begin{array}{r}6\,1\\-2\,3\\\hline 38\end{array}$	$\begin{array}{r}7\,6\\-4\,8\\\hline 28\end{array}$

2 How many more raspberries has Bob?

53 27 $\begin{array}{r}5\,3\\-2\,7\\\hline 26\end{array}$ 53 19 $\begin{array}{r}5\,3\\-1\,9\\\hline 34\end{array}$ 53 35 $\begin{array}{r}5\,3\\-3\,5\\\hline 16\end{array}$

3 Kim picks 81 strawberries.
She eats 27.

How many are left?

$\begin{array}{r}8\,1\\-2\,7\\\hline 54\end{array}$

---

1 81 take away 27.

$\begin{array}{r}8\,1\\-2\,7\\\hline 54\end{array}$

2 61 subtract 16.

$\begin{array}{r}6\,1\\-1\,6\\\hline 45\end{array}$

3 Find the difference between 23 and 72.

$\begin{array}{r}7\,2\\-2\,3\\\hline 49\end{array}$

Jean scored 37. How many more does she need to score 50?

She needs 13 more.

4

5

$\begin{array}{r}7\,7\\-3\,7\\\hline 40\end{array}$	$\begin{array}{r}8\,3\\-4\,6\\\hline 37\end{array}$	$\begin{array}{r}9\,7\\-6\,0\\\hline 37\end{array}$	$\begin{array}{r}6\,6\\-2\,9\\\hline 37\end{array}$	$\begin{array}{r}7\,1\\-3\,4\\\hline 37\end{array}$	$\begin{array}{r}8\,0\\-1\,8\\\hline 62\end{array}$

Each child had a 20p coin to spend.
Use coins to count out the change. Check.

Raj bought 7p   Change

Check $\boxed{13\text{p}}$ $\begin{array}{r}2\,0\text{p}\\-\ 7\text{p}\\\hline 13\text{p}\end{array}$

Vera bought 14p   Change 1p 5p

Check $\boxed{6\text{p}}$ $\begin{array}{r}2\,0\\-1\,4\\\hline 6\text{p}\end{array}$

Sara bought 9p   Change 1p 10p

Check $\boxed{11\text{p}}$ $\begin{array}{r}2\,0\text{p}\\-\ 9\text{p}\\\hline 11\text{p}\end{array}$

Each child had a 50p coin to spend.
Use coins to count out the change. Check.

David bought 38p   Change

Check $\boxed{12\text{p}}$ $\begin{array}{r}5\,0\text{p}\\-3\,8\text{p}\\\hline 12\text{p}\end{array}$

Liam bought 26p   Change 2p 2p 20p

Check $\boxed{24\text{p}}$ $\begin{array}{r}5\,0\text{p}\\-2\,6\text{p}\\\hline 24\text{p}\end{array}$

Diana bought 17p   Change 2p 1p 20p 10p

Check $\boxed{33\text{p}}$ $\begin{array}{r}5\,0\text{p}\\-1\,7\text{p}\\\hline 33\text{p}\end{array}$

55p Magic Mirrors   SPOOKY STORIES 18p   26p HAUNTED HORRORS

1 Which is dearest? *Magic mirrors*

Which is cheapest? *Spooky stories*

Find the difference in price. 37p

2 What is the total cost of the three tickets?

$\begin{array}{r}5\,5\text{p}\\1\,8\text{p}\\+2\,6\text{p}\\\hline 9\,9\text{p}\end{array}$

3 Zara had 90p.
She went to the Magic Mirrors and the Spooky Stories.
How much did she have left? 17p

$\begin{array}{r}5\,5\text{p}\\+1\,8\text{p}\\\hline 7\,3\text{p}\end{array}$ $\begin{array}{r}9\,0\text{p}\\-7\,3\text{p}\\\hline 1\,7\text{p}\end{array}$

Name | Heinemann Mathematics 3 Home Link-up
Textbook pages 13 and 14
Addition and subtraction within 99 | **28**

1 How many children are on each bus?

Happy $\begin{array}{r}4\,2\ \text{girls}\\+3\,8\ \text{boys}\\\hline 80\end{array}$ Sprinter $\begin{array}{r}1\,4\ \text{girls}\\+4\,4\ \text{boys}\\\hline 58\end{array}$ Nippy $\begin{array}{r}1\,9\ \text{girls}\\+2\,9\ \text{boys}\\\hline 48\end{array}$

2 How many more children are on Sprinter than Nippy? 10 more

$\begin{array}{r}5\,8\\-4\,8\\\hline 10\end{array}$

3 Find the difference between the numbers of girls on Happy and Sprinter.

$\begin{array}{r}4\,2\\-1\,4\\\hline 28\end{array}$

4 $63 + 36 = 99$ $27 + 72 = 99$ $45 + 54 = 99$

Write other pairs of numbers like these which total 99. $81 + 18 = 99$

Problem solving

Extra   Tick (✔) the squares which are magic.

23	19	39
43	27 ✔	11
15	35	31

26	20	24
21	23	25
22	26	20

29	36	31
34	32	30
33	28 ✔	35

Name

Heinemann Mathematics 3 Home Link-up
Workbook 2, pages 3 and 4
Multiplication: using the × sign

29

1 Complete.

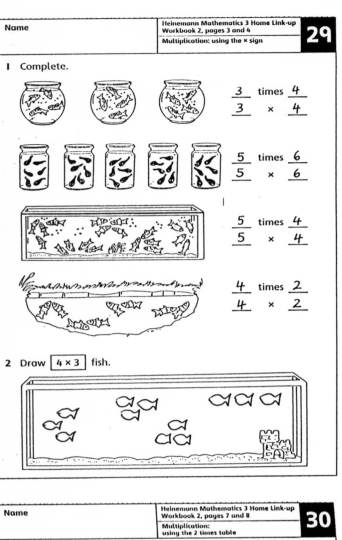

$\underline{3}$ times $\underline{4}$
$\underline{3}$ × $\underline{4}$

$\underline{5}$ times $\underline{6}$
$\underline{5}$ × $\underline{6}$

$\underline{5}$ times $\underline{4}$
$\underline{5}$ × $\underline{4}$

$\underline{4}$ times $\underline{2}$
$\underline{4}$ × $\underline{2}$

2 Draw $\boxed{4 \times 3}$ fish.

Name

Heinemann Mathematics 3 Home Link-up
Workbook 2, pages 9 and 10
Multiplication: using the times table

31

1 Three trays. 4 ants in each.

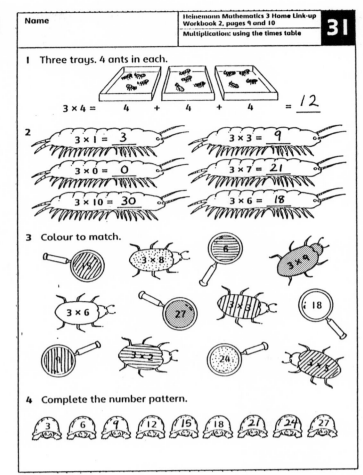

$3 \times 4 =$ $\underline{4}$ + $\underline{4}$ + $\underline{4}$ = $\underline{12}$

2
$3 \times 1 = \underline{3}$ $3 \times 3 = \underline{9}$
$3 \times 0 = \underline{0}$ $3 \times 7 = \underline{21}$
$3 \times 10 = \underline{30}$ $3 \times 6 = \underline{18}$

3 Colour to match.

15 3×8 6 3×9

3×6 27 $3 \times$ 18

3×2 24 $3 \times$

4 Complete the number pattern.

3 6 9 12 15 18 21 24 27

Name

Heinemann Mathematics 3 Home Link-up
Workbook 2, pages 7 and 8
Multiplication:
using the 2 times table

30

1
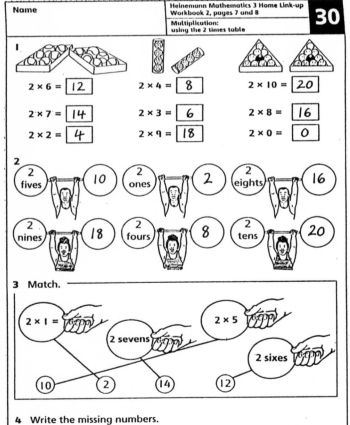

$2 \times 6 = \boxed{12}$ $2 \times 4 = \boxed{8}$ $2 \times 10 = \boxed{20}$
$2 \times 7 = \boxed{14}$ $2 \times 3 = \boxed{6}$ $2 \times 8 = \boxed{16}$
$2 \times 2 = \boxed{4}$ $2 \times 9 = \boxed{18}$ $2 \times 0 = \boxed{0}$

2
2 fives — 10   2 ones — 2   2 eights — 16
2 nines — 18   2 fours — 8   2 tens — 20

3 Match.

$2 \times 1 =$ 2×5
2 sevens   2 sixes
10   2   14   12

4 Write the missing numbers.

2 4 6 8 10 12 14 16 18 20

---

1 How many paints are there on
2 square trays? $\underline{10}$
3 round trays? $\underline{9}$
3 square trays and 2 round trays? $\underline{21}$

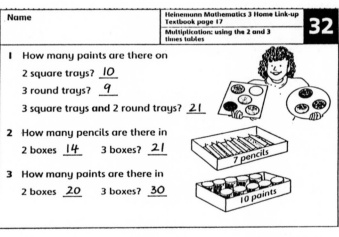

2 How many pencils are there in
2 boxes $\underline{14}$ 3 boxes? $\underline{21}$

7 pencils

3 How many paints are there in
2 boxes $\underline{20}$ 3 boxes? $\underline{30}$

10 paints

---

1 Find the cost of
2 biscuits $\underline{14p}$
3 cakes $\underline{27p}$
3 apples $\underline{12p}$
2 pieces of orange $\underline{16p}$
2 carrots $\underline{12p}$ 3 biscuits $\underline{21p}$
3 pieces of orange and 1 carrot $\underline{30p}$
2 apples and 3 carrots $\underline{26p}$

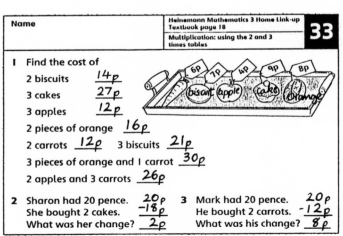

6p 7p 4p 9p 8p
biscuit apple cake orange

2 Sharon had 20 pence. $20p$
She bought 2 cakes. $-18p$
What was her change? $\underline{2p}$

3 Mark had 20 pence. $20p$
He bought 2 carrots. $-12p$
What was his change? $\underline{8p}$

1
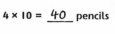

4 × 4 = __16__ rulers

4 × 8 = __32__ paintbrushes

4 × 10 = __40__ pencils

2

4 × 1p = __4__ p   4 × 2p = __8p__   4 × 5p = __20p__

4 × 8p = __32__ p   4 × 7p = __28p__   4 × 9p = __36p__

3 Colour to match.

4 Write the missing numbers.

4	8	12	16	20	24	28	32	36

5 4 × 9 = | 36 | 4 × 0 = | 0 | 4 × 3 = | 12 |

   4 × | 6 | = 24   4 × | 7 | = 28   4 × | 5 | = 20

---

1 Colour to match.

2
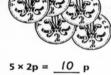

5 × 2p = __10__ p   5 × 5p = __25p__   5 × 10p = __50p__

5 × 3p = __15__ p   5 × 7p = __35p__   5 × 9p = __45p__

3 Join the numbers in order.   4 Complete.

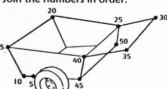

                                        5 × 4 = | 20 |

                                        5 × | 10 | = 40

                                        5 × | 0 | = 0

5 Write the missing numbers.

5 10 15 20 25 30 35 40 45 50

---

5 carrots   7 potatoes   8 tomatoes   6 onions

1 How many?

carrots in 4 bags __20__   potatoes in 5 bags __35__

onions in 4 bags __24__   tomatoes in 5 bags __40__

potatoes in 4 bags __28__   onions in 5 bags __30__

tomatoes in 4 bags __32__   carrots in 5 bags __25__

2

20 turnips altogether.

4 × __5__ = 20

3 5 × | 10 | = 50

   4 × | 9 | = 36

   5 × | 1 | = 5

4 Prices

9p   7p   4p

4 apples cost __36p__   5 oranges cost __35__ p

5 pears cost + __20p__   4 pears cost __16p__

Total cost __56__ p   Total cost __51__ p

---

1 Write each answer.

14	32	27	25
2 × 7	4 × 8	3 × 9	5 × 5

9	20	35	24
3 × 3	10 × 2	5 × 7	4 × 6

Red answers - 14, 32, 20, 24   Blue answers - 27, 25, 9, 35

2 Colour the even answers red and the odd answers blue.

---

1 How many of each does Sarah have?

   2 boxes with 8 vans in each. __16__ vans

   4 boxes with 5 trucks in each. __20__ trucks

   5 boxes with 9 cars in each. __45__ cars

2 Find the cost of

   3 dog stickers __21p__

   2 car stickers __10p__

   4 football stickers __32p__

   10 dog stickers __70p__

   5 football stickers and a car sticker. __45p__

5p   7p   8p

Use cubes, counters or coins.

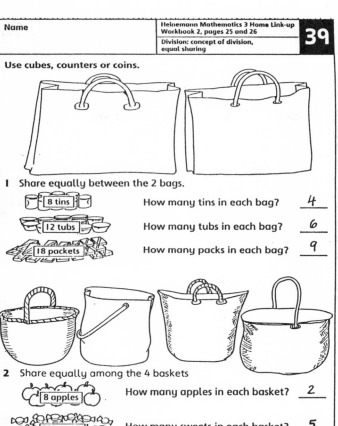

1 Share equally between the 2 bags.

8 tins	How many tins in each bag?	4
12 tubs	How many tubs in each bag?	6
18 packets	How many packs in each bag?	9

2 Share equally among the 4 baskets

8 apples	How many apples in each basket?	2
20 sweets	How many sweets in each basket?	5
16 eggs	How many eggs in each basket?	4

Use cubes, counters or coins.

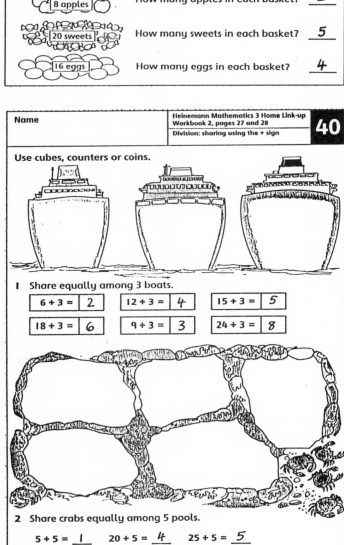

1 Share equally among 3 boats.

| 6 ÷ 3 = | 2 | | 12 ÷ 3 = | 4 | | 15 ÷ 3 = | 5 |
| 18 ÷ 3 = | 6 | | 9 ÷ 3 = | 3 | | 24 ÷ 3 = | 8 |

2 Share crabs equally among 5 pools.

| 5 ÷ 5 = | 1 | | 20 ÷ 5 = | 4 | | 25 ÷ 5 = | 5 |
| 10 ÷ 5 = | 2 | | 15 ÷ 5 = | 3 | | 30 ÷ 5 = | 6 |

Use cubes, counters or coins.

1 Share 9 books equally among 4 children.

How many books for each child? __2__

How many left over? __1__

$9 ÷ 4 =$ __2__ r __1__

2 7 ÷ 2 = __3__ r __1__   18 ÷ 4 = __4__ r __2__

14 ÷ 3 = __4__ r __2__   9 ÷ 2 = __4__ r __1__

13 ÷ 5 = __2 r 3__   11 ÷ 4 = __2 r 3__

3 Tick (✔) if the remainder is 2.

| 8 ÷ 3 ✔ | 15 ÷ 5 | 9 ÷ 5 | 10 ÷ 4 ✔ | 12 ÷ 5 ✔ |

1

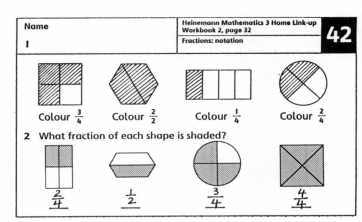

Colour $\frac{3}{4}$ Colour $\frac{2}{2}$ Colour $\frac{1}{4}$ Colour $\frac{2}{4}$

2 What fraction of each shape is shaded?

$\frac{2}{4}$ $\frac{1}{2}$ $\frac{3}{4}$ $\frac{4}{4}$

1 Colour $\frac{1}{2}$ of the cubes.   2 Colour $\frac{1}{2}$ of the cubes.

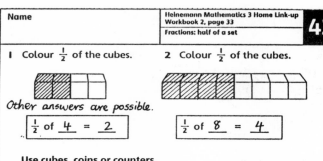

Other answers are possible.

$\frac{1}{2}$ of __4__ = __2__ $\frac{1}{2}$ of __8__ = __4__

Use cubes, coins or counters.

3 $\frac{1}{2}$ of 12 = __6__ $\frac{1}{2}$ of 18 = __9__ $\frac{1}{2}$ of 10 = __5__ $\frac{1}{2}$ of 14 = __7__

4 Tom had 16 sweets. He gave half of them to Sue.
How many did he give to Sue? __8 sweets__

1 Colour $\frac{1}{4}$ of the biscuits.

$\frac{1}{4}$ of __16__ = __4__

Other shadings are possible.

Use cubes, coins or counters.

2 $\frac{1}{4}$ of 24 = __6__ $\frac{1}{4}$ of 32 = __8__

$\frac{1}{4}$ of 40 = __10__ $\frac{1}{4}$ of 20 = __5__

3 Sal had 36 cakes.
She gave one quarter to Jake.
How many did she give to Jake? __9 cakes__

Name

Heinemann Mathematics 3 Home Link-up
Workbook 2, pages 35 and 36
Division: concept of division grouping
45

1 There are 10 children. How many groups of 2? __5__

Use counters, cubes or coins.

2 15 children. How many groups of 3? __5__

How many groups of 5? __3__

3 20 children. How many groups of 5? __4__

How many groups of 4? __5__

How many groups of 2? __10__

---

1 Ring groups of 4.   12 ÷ 4 = __3__

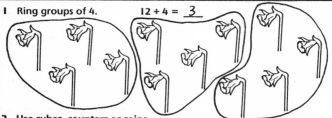

2 Use cubes, counters or coins.

6 ÷ 2 = __3__   8 ÷ 4 = __2__   15 ÷ 5 = __3__

9 ÷ 3 = __3__   10 ÷ 5 = __2__   8 ÷ 2 = __4__

12 ÷ 3 = __4__   16 ÷ 4 = __4__   18 ÷ 3 = __6__

1

How many flowers? __10__

How many groups of 3? __3__

How many left over? __1__

10 ÷ 3 = __3__ r __1__

Use cubes, counters or coins.

2   13 ÷ 4 = __3__ r __1__   12 ÷ 5 = __2__ r __2__

7 ÷ 2 = __3__ r __1__   11 ÷ 3 = __3__ r __2__

14 ÷ 5 = __2 r 4__   15 ÷ 4 = __3 r 3__

---

1 Write each take-off time.

'Plane to	Take-off time			
Aberdeen	10:25	__25__	minutes past	__10__
Belfast	10:50	__50__	minutes past	__10__
Cardiff	11:04	__4__	minutes past	__11__
Dublin	11:30	__30__	minutes past	__11__
Leeds	12:59	__59__	minutes past	__12__

2 Which plane takes off at half past eleven? __Dublin__

3 The Leeds plane took off one minute after 12:59. When did it take off? __1 : 00__

Name

Heinemann Mathematics 3 Home Link-up
MSHD Workbook pages 6 and 7
Time: interpreting analogue times
49

 Fit for Life ♡

The Fun Run started at 3 o'clock.

Zara stopped running after __20__ minutes. The time was __20__ minutes past __3__.

1 The clocks show when some other children stopped running. Write their times.

 Mike stopped running after __39__ minutes.

Tracey stopped running after __54__ minutes.

Time:

__39__ minutes past __3__ .

Time:

__54__ minutes past __3__ .

2 Write the start times for these clubs.

Badminton   **Chess**

__5__ minutes past __4__

__45__ minutes past __4__

Art   **Music**

__17__ minutes past __5__

__50__ minutes past __6__

Write the digital time for each clock.

3 : 20   6 : 50   9 : 17

1 : 47   12 : 30   10 : 34

Write each time: Use quarter past or quarter to.

1:15

__quarter to 12__   __quarter past 1__

 2:45   12:45

__quarter to 3__   __quarter past 4__   __quarter to 1__

1 Write the before and after times.

One hour before	Time	One hour after
half past 2	*(clock)*	half past 4
6:15	7:15	8:15

One hour before	Time	One hour after
3:45	4:45	5:45
11 o'clock	*(clock)*	1 o'clock

2 Find how long each journey took.

11:00 → 2:00   3 hours

_____ → _____   2 hours

Extra

Use a tape which is marked in centimetres.
Measure in centimetres. Ask an adult to check.

around a pot
about _____ cm

height of a chair
about _____ cm

Answers depend on objects selected by the children.

height to your waist
about _____ cm

your reach across a table
about _____ cm

Name

Heinemann Mathematics 3 Home Link-up
MSDH Workbook pages 15 and 16
Area: counting squares, comparison

54

1 Write the area of each letter.

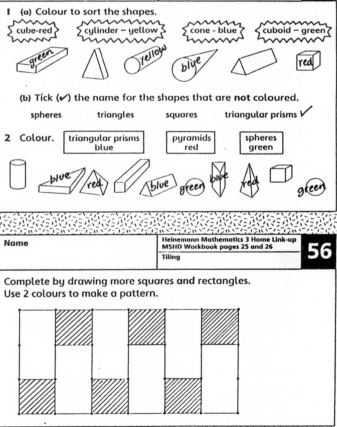

_7_ squares   _10_ squares   _8_ squares   _7_ squares

2 What is the area of this shape?
_9_ squares

Draw a shape with a **smaller** area. Colour it blue.
Draw a shape with a **larger** area. Colour it red.

Blue   red

Other answers are possible.

3 Draw and colour 3 different shapes each with an area of 9 squares.

Other answers are possible.

---

1 Estimate, then measure in centimetres, the height of each flower.

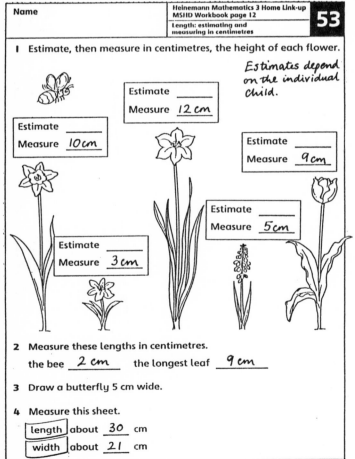

Estimates depend on the individual child.

Estimate _____
Measure _12 cm_

Estimate _____
Measure _10 cm_

Estimate _____
Measure _9 cm_

Estimate _____
Measure _5 cm_

Estimate _____
Measure _3 cm_

2 Measure these lengths in centimetres.

the bee _2 cm_   the longest leaf _9 cm_

3 Draw a butterfly 5 cm wide.

4 Measure this sheet.

length about _30_ cm
width about _21_ cm

---

1 (a) Colour to sort the shapes.

cube-red   cylinder – yellow   cone – blue   cuboid – green

green   yellow   blue   red

(b) Tick (✔) the name for the shapes that are **not** coloured.

spheres   triangles   squares   triangular prisms ✔

2 Colour.

| triangular prisms blue | pyramids red | spheres green |

blue   red   blue   green   blue   red   green

Complete by drawing more squares and rectangles.
Use 2 colours to make a pattern.

1 Shade to make the pattern symmetrical.

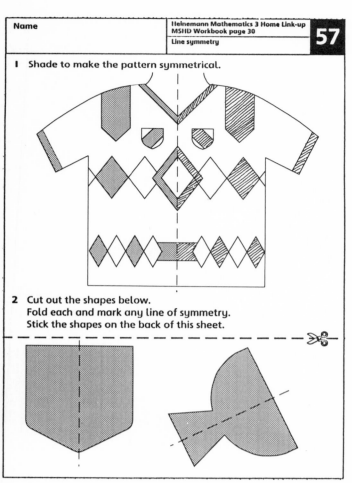

2 Cut out the shapes below.
Fold each and mark any line of symmetry.
Stick the shapes on the back of this sheet.

On the school trip the children bought these things in Sam's café.

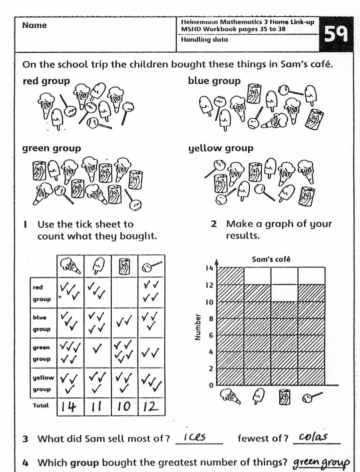

red group   blue group

green group   yellow group

1 Use the tick sheet to count what they bought.

2 Make a graph of your results.

	🍦	🍦	🥤	🍭
red group	✓✓✓✓	✓✓✓		✓✓✓✓
blue group	✓✓✓	✓✓✓✓	✓✓	✓✓✓
green group	✓✓✓✓✓	✓	✓✓✓✓	✓✓✓
yellow group	✓✓✓	✓✓✓	✓✓	✓✓✓✓
Total	14	11	10	12

Sam's café graph

3 What did Sam sell most of? _ices_ fewest of? _colas_

4 Which **group** bought the greatest number of things? _green group_

Use a mirror if you wish.

1 Draw a line of symmetry on each.

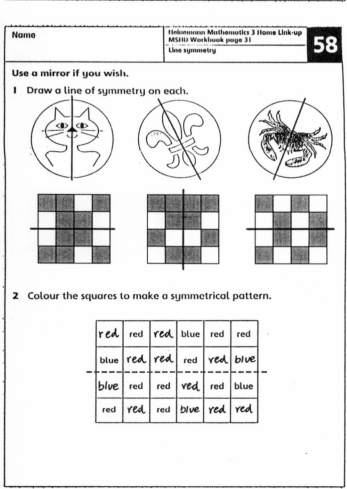

2 Colour the squares to make a symmetrical pattern.

red	red	red	blue	red	red
blue	red	red	red	red	blue
blue	red	red	red	red	blue
red	red	red	blue	red	red

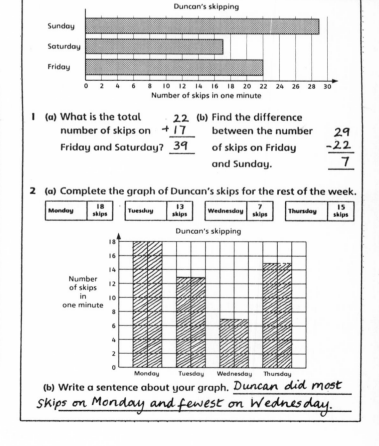

Duncan's skipping

1 (a) What is the total number of skips on Friday and Saturday?

$$\begin{array}{r} 22 \\ +\ 17 \\ \hline 39 \end{array}$$

(b) Find the difference between the number of skips on Friday and Sunday.

$$\begin{array}{r} 29 \\ -22 \\ \hline 7 \end{array}$$

2 (a) Complete the graph of Duncan's skips for the rest of the week.

Monday	18 skips	Tuesday	13 skips	Wednesday	7 skips	Thursday	15 skips

Duncan's skipping

(b) Write a sentence about your graph. _Duncan did most skips on Monday and fewest on Wednesday._